In the City Park

by Claire Daniel
illustrated by Tom Stanley

Orlando Boston Dallas Chicago San Diego

Visit *The Learning Site!*

www.harcourtschool.com

I sell hot dogs in the
city park.
Do you want one?

I pick up in the city park.
Sometimes it's a big
mess!

I stop cars in the city
park.
Do you need help?

4

Sometimes dogs go out.
I take dogs to the city
park.

Sometimes I take people
to the city park.

I make art in the city
park.
Sometimes people sit
for me.

We all have jobs.
We like the city park
a lot.